MISTER CLIP CLOP
INTERGALACTIC
SPACE UNICORN

TONY LEE AND NEIL SLORANCE

LONDON·SYDNEY

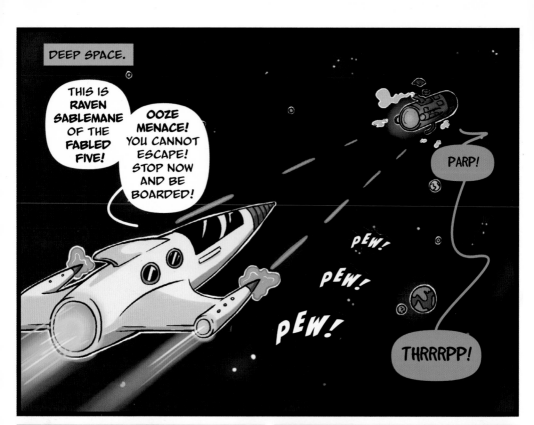

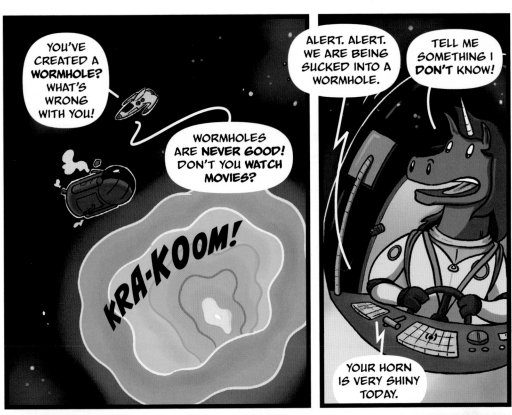

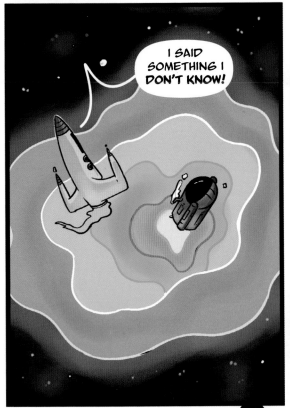

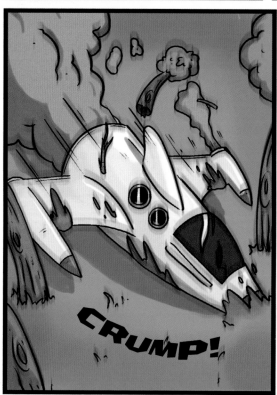

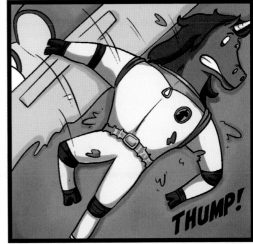

MRS WIGGLESWORTH, WOULD YOU LIKE SOME **CHOCOLATE CAKE?**

NO, YOU ALWAYS HAVE **TOO MUCH,** AND YOUR TUMMY **EXPLODES!**

WAIT - DID YOU SAY **CHOCOLATE CAKE?**

SHE ALWAYS DOES. IT'S HER **FAVOURITE.** WHY?

THE OOZE MENACE HAVE BEEN TO EARTH BEFORE.

THEY LEARNED A SECRET --

CHOCOLATE CAKE CAN **HEAL THEIR WOUNDS!**

IF THEY'RE **INJURED,** THEY WILL FIND SOME.

COME ON! TAKE ME TO THE NEAREST **BAKERY!**

FFZZT!

FFZZT!

HOW ARE YOU **DOING** BACK THERE, BOB?

FINE AND DANDY, MISTER CLIP CLOP!

I MEAN **RAVEN SABLEMANE**, SIR!

MISTER CLIP CLOP IS FINE.

I'VE GOTTEN USED TO IT.

BACK OFF, SABLEMANE! OR WE BLAST THESE TWO HOSTAGES OUT OF AN AIRLOCK!

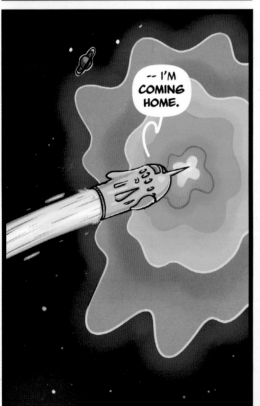

THE END.